321 Creative Writing Prompts

321 Creative Writing Prompts

Lisa Dyer

ARCTURUS

This edition published in 2021 by Arcturus Publishing Limited
26/27 Bickels Yard, 151–153 Bermondsey Street,
London SE1 3HA

ISBN: 978-1-3988-0888-1
AD008846UK

Printed in China

Introduction

Whether your interest is crime or memoir, romance or science fiction, here are hundreds of ideas, story starters and one-liners to help you dive into the creative world of writing. Open to any page and get started on these fun, entertaining and thought-provoking exercises, which will help improve your writing skills, overcome writer's block or inspire that novel you've always been meaning to pen.

Explore your memories, experiences, feelings, observations and imagination to create plotlines, characters, settings, dialogue, moods and more – from the realistic to the fantastical. Dip into different genres and try out crime, reportage, romance, adventure, humour, nature and historical writing. You may find that a character you invent starts to take on a life and story of their own, or a scene can be linked to other circumstances to build a plot line, or a memory is a springboard to an autobiography or family genealogical history. Whatever style you prefer, these writing prompts will stimulate your creativity and spark your storytelling.

Writing Tips

1. Address the five whys: who, what, when, where and why.

2. Consider the reader – why should they care about your protagonist or story?

3. If you aren't feeling the response you want the reader to feel, it's not working. Humorous accounts should make you laugh. Thrillers should evoke fear or trepidation.

4. Revisit your work. Embellish, edit, rework it from a different point of view or transport a character from one story into another setting or time period.

5. Develop your characters with details about their physicality and personality as well as their backstory. Think about where they would live and shop, what they would buy or the kind of car they would drive.

6. Use all five senses, not just the visual, to bring characters and a setting to life.

7. Sharpen your observational skills, taking note of people and situations around you, and weave them into your story writing.

8. Practise writing with short pieces – a six-word story, a 280-character Twitterature, a 50- or 500-word flash fiction.

Write the beginning of a story using these first lines.

As the sun set over the harbour, the lights of the city came on, one by one.

You could say that we were destined to meet.

I don't usually like parties, but I'd just moved into the area and didn't know many people.

Mother hated bad manners, especially in adults.

I never wanted to be President.

It was the knock-out punch that did it.

Begin a story with a funeral – possibly your own, a relative's or a murder victim's. Are you at a church, a wake, a crematorium or a graveside?

Begin a story with a birth. It could be your own, your child's, an historical figure or even an animal's.

Begin a story with a cataclysmic event, such as an earthquake, tsunami, pandemic, alien invasion or a nuclear war.

Begin a story with a wedding that goes wrong.

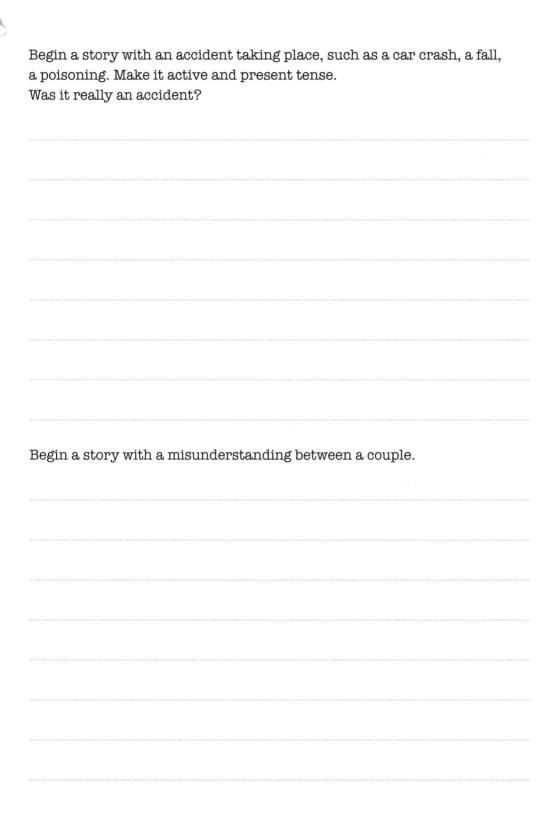

Begin a story with an accident taking place, such as a car crash, a fall, a poisoning. Make it active and present tense.
Was it really an accident?

Begin a story with a misunderstanding between a couple.

Begin a story with a case of mistaken identity.

Begin a story with a theft – perhaps a small act of shoplifting, a major financial fraud, a pick-pocketing or a great art heist.

Write something based on these story starters.

At the top of the building, a person stands on a ledge.

_____

_____

_____

_____

_____

_____

They were playing Truth or Dare. He accepted the dare.

_____

_____

_____

_____

_____

_____

I saw my neighbour digging in his backyard late last night.

The friends were walking along the riverside path when they made an horrific discovery.

Finish these lines.

Jack pulled his car into the patch of waste ground. He reached into the
back seat and...

....

....

....

....

In later years I would come to regret it, but I...

....

....

....

....

The snow was falling fast and we only had a couple hours to...

....

....

....

....

Lexie scanned the horizon, for what seemed like the millionth time...

If it hadn't been for that phone call, I would never...

She stuck her thumb out. This was the first car she'd seen in three hours...

Finish these lines.

Dr Burton gave a sigh, put down the medical chart and said...

I heard shouting and sirens wailing outside, so I turned on the news and...

Amy lunged for the phone; it was her only chance to call...

The train was leaving the station just as he arrived...

....

....

....

....

She reluctantly handed over the keys. Finally, I was able to...

....

....

....

....

Max ran to the centre of the bridge, looked over the parapet and...

....

....

....

....

Write about your first date. Your first kiss.

Tell the story of how you met your best friend or romantic partner.

Describe your childhood pet – its personality, traits, appearance and behaviour.

Remember an item you've lost – a piece of jewellery, a toy, a favourite mug. Why was it significant? How did it get lost?

What is your earliest memory?

What are five things you could do as a child that you can't do now?

Did you ever want to run away from home as a child? If you did run away, what made you leave and how far did you get?

Think of a place you went to as a child and recreate it here – it could be a holiday destination or something simple like a local sweet shop or park.

Remember someone cooking in your childhood kitchen. Describe the smells, sounds and feelings you had. Who is cooking?

What kind of child were you? Shy, bossy, sporty, social or a loner? Write about your personality then, and how or if it's changed.

What was your favourite toy as a child? Describe its shape, texture and the feelings you had about it.

Write about a school friend you have lost contact with.

How did you get to school as a child – by bus, train, walking, driving, skateboarding, cycling? Describe the journey and what you did on the way.

....

....

....

....

....

Write about the most popular girl or boy in your school.

....

....

....

....

....

Describe a memorable teacher.

What was your most-hated class at school – PE, maths, languages?
Re-live the feelings of dread, in the knowledge that you got through it.

Where did you live growing up? A city, village, farm, town, countryside, suburb – and what did and didn't you like about it?

What was the first night you spent away from your childhood home?

What was – or is – your favourite family tradition?

What career did you want to have when you were a child and why?

What was your first job and what did you love or hate about it?

Did you ever have a nickname or give someone else a nickname?
Why, and what did it mean?

What model was your first bicycle or car and how did you get it?
Describe your first feeling of freedom and where you went.

What song brings back memories for you? Where did you hear it and what sensations and feelings does it evoke?

Write about the most embarrassing thing that happened to you.

Write about the funniest thing that happened to you.

Rewrite your own history. How would your life be different if one significant event (a house move, a family divorce, a bereavement) never happened?

Who do you wish you could bring back from the dead? Write about your memories of them and what they might say about being here now.

Describe an accident you were in or a dangerous situation you avoided or survived.

What was the best party you ever went to? Where was it, what happened and who was there?

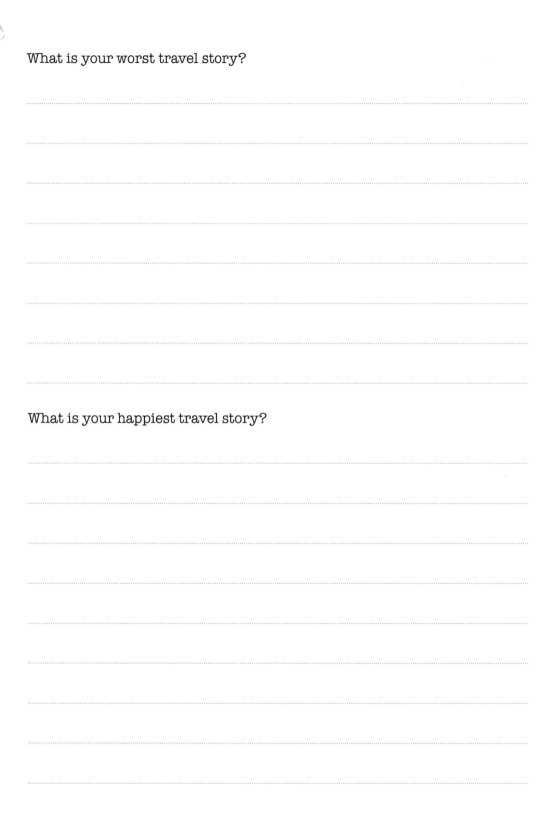

What is your worst travel story?

What is your happiest travel story?

Write about the worst haircut you ever had.

Write about your best restaurant experience and describe the setting, food and people.

If your house could talk, what would it say about its past?

Write about a favourite item of clothing you had – how it looked, felt and smelled, and its significance to you.

What is the best advice you were ever given and who gave it?

Write your own eulogy.

Write a legacy letter, listing a few of the things you'd want someone to know about your life once you are gone – such as a family anecdote, a cherished memory or a life lesson you want to impart.

What memories do you associate with the following smells

Cut grass

....

....

Bleach

....

....

Lemons

....

....

Cinnamon

....

....

Coffee

....

....

Mint or peppermint

....

....

Pine trees

....

....

Baking bread

....

....

Stale beer

....

....

Frying bacon

....

....

What are you most scared of? Snakes, flying, small spaces, going blind? Describe your fear.

Write about your happiest moment.

What makes you angry? It could be a person, situation or event.

Write about the bravest thing you've ever done.

Some emotions are hard to write about because they aren't dynamic – so you need to show the emotion, rather than tell. Try it with these exercises.

Describe a guilty person, how they look, sound and behave.

....

....

....

....

....

....

Describe what a person looks like when they are bored.

....

....

....

....

....

....

Now describe a sad or grieving person.

_____

_____

_____

_____

_____

_____

_____

Now try a confident person.

_____

_____

_____

_____

_____

_____

_____

_____

Write about a time you had to forgive someone.

Write about a time you had to ask for forgiveness.

What is your biggest regret?

What makes you excited and full of energy and anticipation?

....

....

....

....

What makes you jealous of others?

....

....

....

....

Write about your proudest achievement and how you felt.

....

....

....

....

Who has done you wrong, cheated, bullied, rejected, betrayed, lied to or hurt you? Describe the event and your feelings.

Now plot your revenge.

Write about the first time you fell in love.

List 20 things you love that aren't people.

You have been stranded alone on Mars. You have food and shelter, but won't be rescued for another six months. How are you feeling? What do you miss most?

You have just won two million in the lottery. Describe your emotions. What will you do with the money?

You have just been told you only have five years left to live. How do you feel and what do you do?

Similes can be powerful ways to describe emotions. Write as many similes as you can to describe how much you love (or hate, or are indifferent to) someone, taking Robert Burns' famous line, 'O my love is like a red, red rose', as inspiration.

My love is like...

Open a kitchen cupboard at random. Describe what you see.

Describe the last meal you ate, including details of the temperature, smell, taste and texture.

Write about an afternoon walk you took, and who and what you saw – from a dog's perspective.

Choose a country or city you've never been to and write about why you want to visit it, or why you don't.

Look at a tree in your garden or local park, noticing the colours, textures and foliage. Describe everything you see. Next, write about how the same tree looks in a different season.

Imagine you are alone in a forest. Describe everything you hear. Then describe everything you smell.

Write down every adjective you can to describe the weather today.

You find a nest in the branch of a tree – what's inside?

Write a short piece in which Mother Nature is the narrator.
What does she have to say?

Visit an outdoor space in the morning and write a paragraph about what you see. Revisit the same spot at night and write another paragraph.

Choose a body of water – a sea, lake, river or stream, in your imagination or in real life – and write about where it is, what it looks like, the sounds and smells, the tides and currents.

Now write about a person, or persons, interacting with the water – either for work or recreation.

Where in nature do you feel safest? Or unsafest?

What makes you feel part of the natural world? In what way do you feel separate from the natural world?

Imagine you are a wild animal in the city. Try to capture the feeling of alienation that comes with being in a place that's not your natural habitat.

Imagine you are an animal in a herd – a cow or a bird, domesticated or wild. How does it feel to belong to a group, or to be under threat as a group

Write about your favourite season.

Describe the view from your bedroom window.

Use at least three of the following words in a piece of writing:
blue coat, karma, stormy, bicycle, grass, sailboat, hungry, radiator,
scream, glass.

Take a couple minutes to listen to the sounds around you: a ticking clock,
an overhead airplane, nearby voices. Now write the ideas or feelings one
or more of those sounds evoke.

You see an unusually dressed person on the bus. Describe what they are wearing. Where do you imagine they are going?

What do shoes tell you about a person? Note the shoes of someone you see and write about that person.

....

....

....

....

....

Describe the strangest person you ever met. Explore the defining characteristics that stood out, such as a physical feature, a way of speaking, a mannerism.

....

....

....

....

Describe yourself to someone who has never met you.

....

....

....

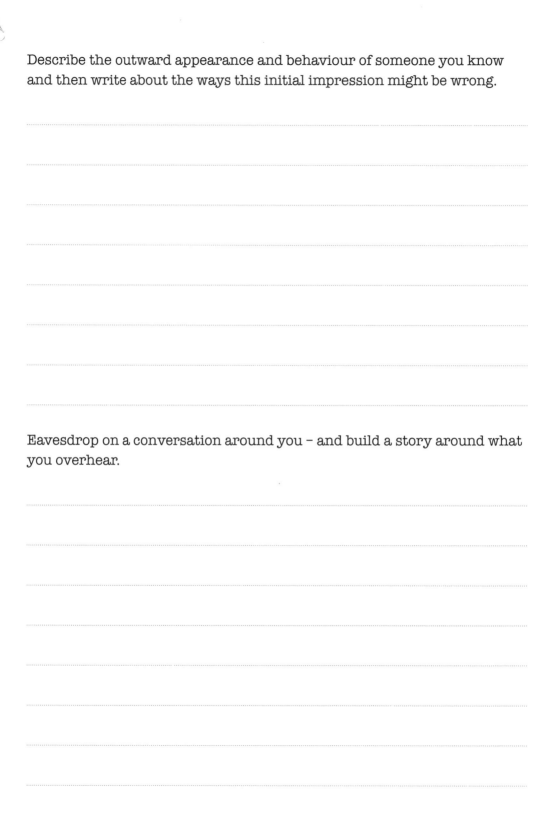

Describe the outward appearance and behaviour of someone you know and then write about the ways this initial impression might be wrong.

Eavesdrop on a conversation around you – and build a story around what you overhear.

Describe a fishing town from the point of view of a sailor who visits it once a month.

Describe the wedding dress of a socialite for a bridal magazine.

Describe your favourite colour to a someone who can't see.

Describe the sky after a storm.

Describe a family member to a stranger – one of your parents, a sibling or your crazy aunt or uncle.

Describe rush hour at a busy train station – the noise, the smells, the action.

Your see your friend's new-born baby for the first time. Describe your thoughts, feelings and impressions.

You are the sober wallflower at a lively, drunken cocktail party. What do you observe?

You are the doorman for a luxury hotel in the city. What do you see every day?

Now, what if you were the receptionist at a seedy motel?

Imagine you are the wicked stepmother in a fairy tale. What are your evil plans?

You are a doctor in a hospital's Accident and Emergency department Describe a day in your life.

You are a famous celebrity. Describe a day in your life.

A man lights a large bonfire in a clearing. What is he burning?

A retired military general has a secret past. What is it?

A stunt double gets mistaken for his famous doppelgänger and begins to pass himself off as the celebrity. How far does he get?

A scuba diver has just discovered a sunken ship with untouched treasure. What does she do next?

Your grandmother has only a short time left to live but has an important message for you. What does she say?

....

....

....

....

A gymnast has dedicated her life to training for the Olympics.
She finally qualifies, achieves a Gold and fulfils her greatest ambition.
Why is she unsatisfied?

....

....

....

....

A popular self-help guru has a manifesto that advocates world peace.
But this isn't the real motivation for what he does. What is?

....

....

....

....

Write the backstory of a high-society con artist who makes a living selling fake masterpieces by great artists.

Your character has just been elected Prime Minister. What are her greatest strengths and why? What weakness is her undoing?

....

....

....

....

Use at least three of these negative adjectives to describe a character: irritable, arrogant, combative, careless, temperamental, greedy, deceitful, cowardly.

....

....

....

....

Use at least three of these positive adjectives to describe a character: generous, fun-loving, breath-taking, witty, reliable, courageous, insightful, honest.

....

....

....

Your character is a 39-year-old serial killer who has never been caught. Describe him in detail, including his hair style and colour, height and build, physical features, clothing and shoes, level of grooming/cleanliness, health, walking pace, voice.

Your dog is recovering from surgery and must wear a cone collar.
Write about how he feels from his perspective.

A climber is on the side of a mountain, the summit within reach.
His fingers are numb, he's exhausted and every foothold seems to
miss its mark. What's going through his mind?

The protagonist in your story has a strange affliction. What is it and how do they overcome it to reach their goals?

Create a superhero and his or her arch enemy.

You are a musician. Give your band a name and write an advertisement for its first appearance.

A respected music critic has just seen your band – what review do they write?

What is your favourite food? Write convincing reasons why everyone should like it too.

If you live in a city, write about why country living is better. If you live in the country, champion city living.

Write an angry letter to a person or institution. Explain in detail the reasons for your anger; cast blame, point fingers and be as vindictive as you dare.

What is the last movie you watched? Write a review. How many stars do you give it?

In the character of a food critic, write a fair review of a local pizza restaurant that had previously failed a health and safety inspection.

Write a literary review of your favourite novel. What was the most compelling thing about the book?

You've just received an Oscar nomination. Prepare your acceptance speech.

Write a love letter to an unrequited love.

A local politician has been caught in a financial scandal. Write the headline and first lines of the story that appears in the newspaper.

You can see into the future and know that a plane crash will happen. You go to the airport to warn the pilot and passengers. How do you convince them to abort the flight?

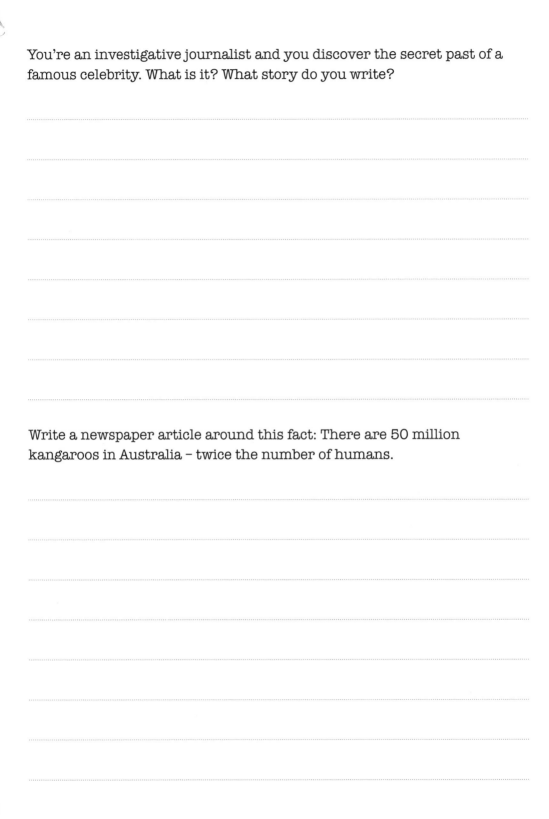

You're an investigative journalist and you discover the secret past of a famous celebrity. What is it? What story do you write?

Write a newspaper article around this fact: There are 50 million kangaroos in Australia – twice the number of humans.

Write the directions for the walk from your house to a local landmark, such as a church, post office or bus stop. Include everything you see on the way.

Write an advertisement for selling your pet snake.

Write the instructions for how to use a rubber band. Include all its merits –
and why alternatives, such as string and paper clips, are poor substitutes.

Write a glowing review for your friend's rental property that she can post
online.

Now write a negative review.

Your neighbour plays music that keeps you awake all night. Write him a letter of complaint, making sure you tell him exactly why his preferred genre of music is so irritating.

Write a review of a local attraction – such as an art gallery, museum or park.

Open your refrigerator. Devise a recipe using one item you see.

Write an effusive description of a new champagne, wine or beer that's just been launched.

Write the general instructions for a sport you know and love, such as football or tennis, as if describing it to someone who knows nothing about the game.

A dead body has been discovered in a house. As the first detective on the scene, write up a crime report detailing everything you see.

A new animal has been discovered. What is its appearance, features, habitat and behaviour? What does it eat, where does it sleep?
Is it dangerous or meek, fast-footed or slow?

A letter arrives from a long-lost sister. What does it say?

Write a 'Dear John' breakup letter.

You are able to travel back to one day in your life. What day do you choose, why, and what – if anything – do you change?

Reverse the chronology of your life, starting with your death and working back to the day you were born.

Imagine you could be in two places at once. Where would you be and how might those two storylines merge?

Write down the last thing you think of before you fall asleep. What does this tell you about yourself?

If you had to immediately leave your home forever, which five things would you take with you (excluding people or pets)? Why?

If you woke up and discovered you could no longer speak, describe how you would learn to communicate with others?

If you were an animal, what would you be and why?

If you had the ability to read other people's thoughts, how would you use your superpower?

What would you do if your entire online identity disappeared?

You are found wandering in a city with amnesia. Do you trust what people tell you? How do you rediscover who you are?

What if humans had always been vegan? What would the animal world be like?

What would happen if the world experienced a great flood?

If the Moon was a popular holiday destination, what would you be able to do there?

If you learned that everyone who ever lived is still here in spirit, but we just can't see them, how would you make contact?

Choose an ordinary, everyday object and imagine how it was used in a crime.

....

....

....

....

....

Every night you see a bright light shining from a derelict building. You decide to investigate. What do you find?

....

....

....

....

....

....

You've woken from a coma after six years. What happened to you?

You visit a fortune-teller and they tell you something that later comes true. What is it?

You have discovered why planes mysteriously disappear in the Bermuda Triangle. What is it?

A kind, quiet librarian is mixed up in a high-profile murder. How did she get involved?

You have just discovered hidden surveillance cameras in your home. Who has been watching you and *why*?

A gentleman you never heard of leaves you a valuable object in his will. Describe how you'd find out why.

An elderly couple in a retirement home are revealed as the masterminds behind a string of jewel thefts. What's their story?

You wake up with no memory of the previous evening, but you then start receiving blackmail text messages, threatening to expose what you did. Work backwards to recover your memory and discover what happened.

A deep-voiced man keeps calling on the house phone, asking for your wife. How do you find out who he is and what he wants?

Your husband's trips out of town are getting more frequent. One day you follow him. What do you discover?

A man meets an ex-lover for lunch. They haven't seen each other in ten years. What happens next?

A game of tennis brings two unlikely people together. Describe how the game develops.

What do you do when you receive an intimate text message from your wife, meant for your best friend?

A couple meets in Las Vegas and spontaneously decides to get married that night. What do they discover about each other in the cold light of day?

You fell down a ravine during a country walk, sprained your ankle and are now lost in the woods. How do you find your way back out?

You and a friend decide to go on a road trip across country in your old, rusty, broken-down car. Describe your journey.

A conservationist tracking down a rare bird in the rainforest hears an ominous rustling in the undergrowth. What is it, and is she in danger?

A couple wakes up to discover their campsite had been ransacked by bears. What do they do to make it back to safety?

You wake up to discover you are 100 years in the future. What is life like?

Your pet cat is suddenly able to communicate. Recount your conversation with it.

You find a Roman coin in a dry riverbed and discover it has magical powers. What do you do with the coin?

A group of friends find a vinyl record and a record-player in an attic. When they play the albums backwards what message does it reveal that is directed specifically at them?

Describe a new planet – are there seas and land masses? Now populate it with beings – are they human, mammal, reptilian or something completely new?

Devise a quest that your main character must go on in order to save her people.

You are in hiking gear and walking along a remote path. What is the terrain like? Mountainous? Tropical? Where are you going?

You buy a crystal ball in an antique shop and discover that it can help you see into other people's futures but not your own. How do you use your new, unexpected power?

Try giving these story-starters a humorous twist.

There's a freak accident at the bowling alley.

A fast-food restaurant burger-flipper becomes a five-star Michelin chef.

The office practical joker becomes the victim of one of his pranks.

A fussy, fastidious germophobe character is forced to make a month-long road trip by coach.

A set of twins, unhappy with their lives, decide to swap identities. Is the grass greener on the other side?

A dating app completely mismatches two of its users who are polar opposites in every respect.

You can invite three people from history to dinner. Who do you choose and what happens during the meal?

Write the journal entry of an historical figure, such as Napoleon Bonaparte, Marie Antoinette, George Washington, Charles Darwin or Florence Nightingale.

It's the 1600s and you are on trial, accused of witchcraft and facing the death penalty. Defend yourself in court.

You're a small-time wheeler-dealer whose business is not entirely crooked but not completely legal. What do you do when the police raid your warehouse?

A 1920s' Jazz Age nightclub performer is getting ready to go onstage when there is a knock at her dressing-room door. Who is it and what do they want?

You're an aristocrat in hiding during the French Revolution and an angry mob has just discovered your secret location. How do you escape their clutches?

You are a fashion designer in London in the Swinging Sixties – what have you just invented to rival the mini skirt?

Two people are going on a date in the 1950s. Who are they, what are they wearing and where do they meet?

Use all your senses of smell, touch, taste and hearing to describe the following scenes.

A busy kitchen in a restaurant

A dentist's waiting room

A nightclub at 3 am

A library

A fish market

Pick a location from the following list and add details of the time of day, weather, lighting and objects or furnishings: a water park, a high-rise office, a nail salon, a cave, a turret in a castle, an abandoned building, a prison cell, a theatre, a treehouse, the Moon.

Write a scene that takes place in an abandoned mountain cabin between two or more people.

Two lovers meet at a seaside restaurant. There's a storm brewing outside. Describe what happens when they decide to stay put, or if they try to leave when the wind and rain are at their worst.

A child has been lost at a summer camp. Have they been taken? Do they get found?

Why are you on your own in a seedy bar, having a drink? What do you do when a mass brawl breaks out?

You're walking along a river and, in the distance, you see someone fall into the water. What happens next?

You are driving a car in heavy snow and you can't see ahead. You hear a loud honking of horns behind you. Who is it? What do they want?

A lift is stuck between floors in a tall office building. How do the lift's six passengers deal with the situation. Was the lift breaking down deliberate or simply an accident?

A lion escapes from its cage in a packed circus. What happens next?

Write about a botanist that lives on a dying planet.

Write the script for the final shoot-out scene in a spaghetti western.

Write a paragraph about the last song you listened to.

Write about a pilot who develops a fear of flying.

You're packing for a trip – what's in your suitcase?

....

....

....

....

You've lost everything in a poker game and have nothing more to bet. How do you get your money back?

....

....

....

....

You've discovered a secret room in your home. What is its purpose?

....

....

....

....

You've been arrested for a crime. You're guilty and your lawyer knows it.
What's your alibi?

You've been a victim of a rumour – 90 per cent of it is false but there's some truth in it. What's the rumour, and does the 10 per cent of truth reflect badly or well on you?

You have to choose between the person you love and saving a city from imminent disaster. What do you do – and how do you justify your decision?

You pick up the wrong suitcase at the airport. What do you find when you open it and what do you do next?

You're a contract killer and someone has just hired you – who is the target?

A chance encounter with a former roommate brings a long-forgotten event to the surface?

A party is in full swing when it's interrupted by an unwelcome guest. What do they say or do that changes everything?

A reporter presenting the evening news is shocked to read a name she recognizes from the teleprompter. Who is it? Why are they in the news and how will it affect the reporter?

A country's president is just coming off stage when there's a commotion among their secret service protection squad. What is going on?

You get a knock on your front door. A police officer asks you to come with him. Why?

A trove of lost love letters from 40 years ago is found. How does it lead to a reconciliation?

Write a story that takes place in just 10 minutes.

Write a story that takes place over 24 hours.

Write about someone who keeps falling asleep when you talk to them.

Write a story about a lucky escape or near-death experience.

Write about a character who keeps receiving mysterious unsigned letters.

Write about someone who decides to reject modern society and goes to live off-grid.

Write a scene about a woman escaping her criminal past.

Write a scene set in an underground bunker.

Write a story that takes place on a boat at sea.

Write a scene starting with these sentences.

No one in his family supported his ambition to become an undertaker.

They did not find the hotel in the usual way. For a start, there were no road markers or signposts leading to it.

Both his wife and daughter despised him.

We were all disoriented from the freezing cold and lack of sleep.

Write a scene starting with these sentences.

Lucy held tightly on to Sam's hand. She was terrified but tried not to show it.

_____

_____

_____

_____

_____

I put the folder on the table and said to the detective, 'I believe this is what you are looking for.'

_____

_____

_____

_____

_____

Jamie finally arrived at 2 am – no luggage or coat but with a black eye and a fat lip.

Sarah had been dishonourably discharged from the Army, but she would not tell us why.

Finish these lines.

I looked at the label of the medicine bottle and suddenly remembered that...

I didn't want to admit it, but...

Aunt Sally carefully patted down the earth around the...

Behind the fence, the snarling dog...

....

....

....

....

The housekeeper unlocked the front door, stepped into the hallway and...

....

....

....

....

With her ear to the door, Katie could just make out the muffled voices saying...

....

....

....

....

A man enters a confessional in a church. What does he tell the priest?

You have been caught cheating on a test. What lie do you tell to get out of trouble?

You are unexpectedly reunited with an old friend. What do you say to each other?

Two strangers are sitting next to each other on the train. What do they start talking about?

A couple are having an argument. One is angry and the other is calm.
Transcribe their conversation.

Write a scene in which two lovers meet for one last time before they are shipped off to war.

Respond to these conversation starters – keep them going back and forth, between two or more people, as long as you can.

'I thought you said you could cook?'

'You shouldn't be scared of this injection – you're a doctor, after all.'

'Hello. I'm calling about your advertisement.'

'I heard the baby isn't even his.'

'I have something to tell you that's going to be hard to hear.'

'If you want me to help you, you'll have to tell me where the money is.'

'That's ridiculous. They can't arrest you for that!'

'Don't look now but he's staring at you.'

'She's definitely lost ten pounds. She's a total fanatic now.'

'I was doing so well without you.'

'I know this sounds like a cliché, but do you come here often?'

'How long would it take us to drive to the border if we left now?'

A tycoon is on his deathbed, surrounded by his many heirs. What are his last words?

A person convicted of murder is facing the death penalty. What does he or she say to his executioner?

Describe a scene where a dead relative leads you to the afterlife.

Describe an out-of-body experience – your body may be dying or alive, in a hospital setting or going about your daily life.

Closing lines: finish these story endings.

You may think I'm crazy, and this story can't be true, but...

....

....

....

....

....

....

....

Events unfolded the way they had to. In the end, I had no choice because...

....

....

....

....

....

....

....

....

The wind was howling and the earth was cracking under our feet, but we ran towards each other, each of us hoping against hope that...

In the churchyard, there were ten newly-dug graves...

She lifted the gun and took aim. He was right in the crosshairs...

Was what I did justified? You might say it was retribution for the wrong I suffered, or...

Then, before I realized what I was doing, I was on my feet...

The moral of this story is...

They say there are no happy endings in real life, but...

Tomorrow things may be different; tonight...

You may ask if she really died or...

It's all a game that was played...

It all began when...